AN ANGEL VISITS MARY

An angel visits Mary. She is amazed. The angel tells her that she is going to have a baby by the power of God. It will be a son, the Saviour of the world, the Son of God. His name will be Jesus.

Each shadow has been drawn twice except one. Which one is it?

CW00840850

A

B

C

D

E

F

G

There is nothing that God cannot do.
(Luke 1, v37)

3

AN ANGEL APPEARS TO JOSEPH

Mary is expecting a baby even though she is not yet married to Joseph. What a difficult situation to be in ....

Help Joseph to see clearly by arranging the bubbles in the right order.

LEAVING FOR BETHLEHEM

The young married couple live in Nazareth. Mary is about to give birth. The Emperor wants to count how many people live in his kingdom so Mary and Joseph have to go to Bethlehem for the census.

Do your own census of what you see on this page. How many are there?

- *men?*

- *women?*

- *children?*

- *animals?*

THE BIRTH OF JESUS

Many people have come to Bethlehem for the census. Mary is tired but there is no room in any of the inns. Mary and Joseph shelter in a stable, where Mary gives birth to Jesus.

Join the dots 1 to 54 to find out where Mary lays Jesus down.

"A child has been born for us. We have been given a son who will be our ruler."
(Isaiah 9, v 6)

A MESSAGE FOR THE SHEPHERDS

Some shepherds are in the fields when an angel appears to them.

Help the shepherds to find their way to Jesus.

THE SHEPHERDS' VISIT

The shepherds find Jesus and tell Mary and Joseph that an angel had told them about him. They are very happy.

The sheep are happy too! They are all over the place. How many can you find?

THE WISE MEN AND THE STAR

Far away from Bethlehem, the wise men discover a very bright new star in the sky. It leads them to Jesus.

Which route should the wise men take?

"We saw his star in the east and have come to worship him." (Matthew 2, v 2)

A B C D E

JERUSALEM

One month after his birth, Mary and Joseph take Jesus to the temple to present him to God. This was the custom for all children. That day Simeon is in the temple. God had made him a promise that he would see Jesus. Simeon takes the baby in his arms.

Find out what makes Simeon so happy.

(............ 2, 29–30)

To help you

A=   L=   S=

D=   M=   T=

E=   N=   U=

H=   O=   V=

I=   P=   W=

K=   R=   Y=

THE WISE MEN BRING THEIR GIFTS

After a long journey the wise men find Jesus, the king foretold by the prophets. They bow down in front of him and give him wonderful presents.

Colour in the picture following this code.
1 – purple, 2 – blue, 3 – green, 4 – brown, 5 – red, 6 – yellow, 7 – orange

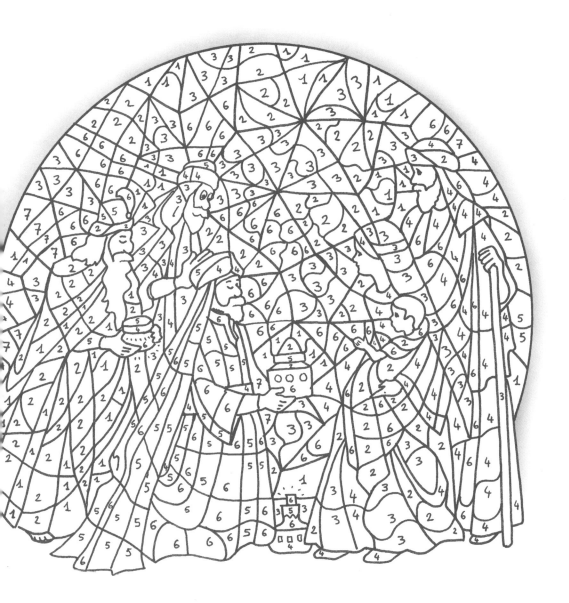

11

FOLLOW THE STAR

To play this game, take a counter or a coin per player and a dice.

Each player throws the dice in turn and moves forward the number of boxes indicated by the dice. A 6 allows you to have an extra turn. The first player to reach the stable is the winner!

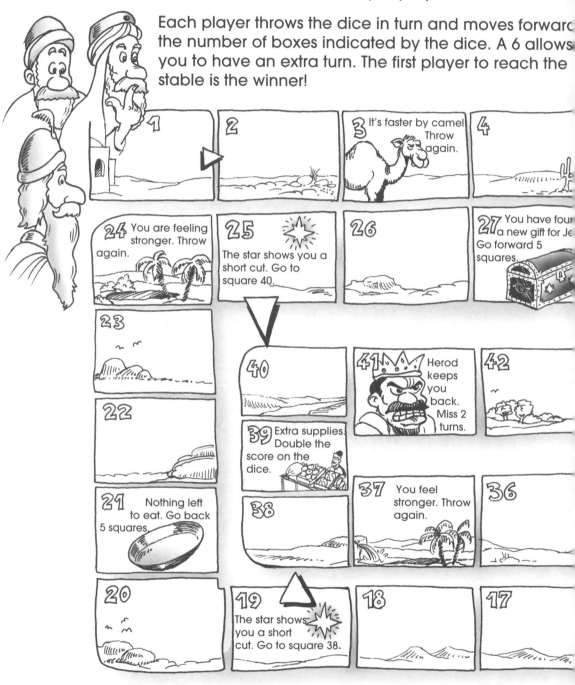

1

2

3 It's faster by camel. Throw again.

4

24 You are feeling stronger. Throw again.

25 The star shows you a short cut. Go to square 40.

26

27 You have found a new gift for Je Go forward 5 squares.

23

22

21 Nothing left to eat. Go back 5 squares.

20

40

39 Extra supplies. Double the score on the dice.

38

19 The star shows you a short cut. Go to square 38.

41 Herod keeps you back. Miss 2 turns.

42

37 You feel stronger. Throw again.

36

18

17

ESCAPE TO EGYPT

King Herod wants to kill Jesus. An angel warns Joseph in a dream and tells him to escape to Egypt. The whole family escapes. About two years later, Herod dies and the angel appears to Joseph again in a dream. He tells him to go back home. Mary, Joseph and Jesus go back to Galilee.

Find the 13 differences between the two pictures below.

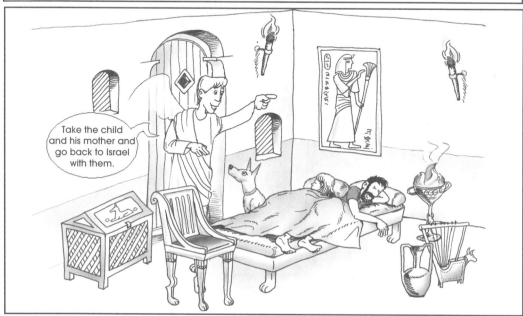

"Out of Egypt I called my son."
(Hosea 11, v 1)

THE CHILD JESUS

After these journeys, Jesus' life is more peaceful. He grows up in Nazareth in Galilee.

Put the towns in the correct places.
To do this, follow the directions and look at the compass.
The town furthest north is Cana.
Tiberias is on the shore of Lake Galilee.
The town furthest south is Bethlehem.
Jerusalem is the closest town to Bethlehem, to the north of it. Nazareth is to the south of Cana. The town nearest to the Dead Sea, and to the north of it, is Jericho.
Samaria is halfway between Nazareth and Jerusalem.

Now draw a line between Nazareth and Jerusalem. Measure it against the scale on the map. How many kilometres as the crow flies did Mary, Joseph and Jesus travel?

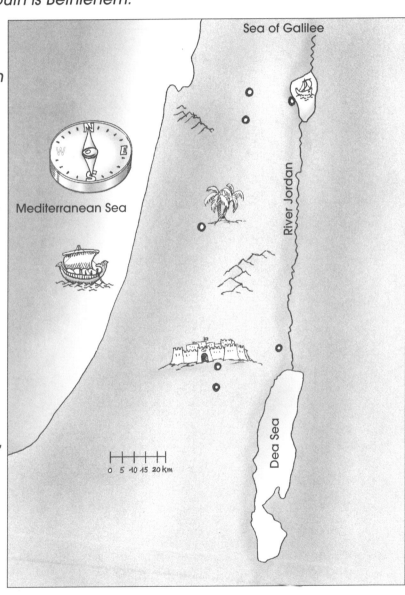

A GOOD EDUCATION

Like all children of his age, Jesus goes to school and has religious teaching. Each week, he goes to the synagogue. He is well behaved and helpful. He likes to help everyone, especially his parents.

What is Jesus doing? FInd out by joining the dots 1 to 69 and A to R.

"Jesus became wise, and he grew strong. God was pleased with him and so were the people." (Luke 2, v 52)

JESUS IN THE TEMPLE

Mary and Joseph go to the temple for the Feast of the Passover. Jesus is 12 years old and he goes with them. After the Feast is over, everyone returns home. On the way back, Mary and Joseph cannot find Jesus. He is in the temple, amazing everyone with his wisdom and knowledge of the scriptures. When Mary and Joseph find him, they all make their way back to the line of pilgrims.

Look for Jesus in the line of pilgrims. He:
- is in front of a child
- is behind a child
- is in front of a donkey
- has nothing in his hands
- is wearing a long tunic

A LARGE FAMILY

Jesus grows up in his village surrounded by his family and a large number of children.

Joseph needs help so he calls four boys. They are far away and do not hear him very well.
Change the letters into the correct order to find out their names.

DO YOU KNOW HOW CHRISTMAS IS DESCRIBED IN THE BIBLE?

Tick the correct answer.

The Bible tells us that:

1 – Jesus was born on 25 December?   ☐ Yes   ☐ No
2 – Jesus was born in Bethlehem?   ☐ Yes   ☐ No
3 – Jesus was born in a stable?   ☐ Yes   ☐ No
4 – A donkey and a cow were there?   ☐ Yes   ☐ No
5 – Jesus was lying in a manger?   ☐ Yes   ☐ No
6 – The first people who went to see Jesus were the shepherds?   ☐ Yes   ☐ No
7 – The angel appeared to the shepherds at night?   ☐ Yes   ☐ No
8 – The wise men were kings?   ☐ Yes   ☐ No
9 – The wise men were called Caspar, Balthazar and Melchior?   ☐ Yes   ☐ No

10 – The wise men came at the beginning of January?   ☐ Yes   ☐ No

11 – Palestine was under the rule of
a) the Romans   ☐
b) the Gauls   ☐

12 – The wise men offered gold, frankincense and myrrh?   ☐ Yes   ☐ No

13 – In an attempt to get rid of Jesus, King Herod had all the children under two years of age killed   ☐ Yes   ☐ No

19

ANSWERS TO THE TEST

1 No
The Bible does not give the exact date that Jesus was born. The decision to celebrate Christmas on 25 December was made around 350 AD. But it is unlikely that this event took place in December, because it is too cold for sheep to stay outside at night in the Bethlehem area. The precise date is not as important as knowing about and understanding what we are celebrating on that day.

2 Yes
Jesus' birth in Bethlehem is foretold in the Old Testament, many years before the actual event. This town lies about ten kilometres away from Jerusalem. (Micah 5, v 2)

3 Yes
His parents, Mary and Joseph, were travelling. There was no room for them in the inn at Bethlehem. They had to stay in a stable, perhaps belonging to the inn. Stables were often under the house, sometimes even in caves. (Luke 2, v 1–7)

4 No
The Bible does not mention them. There may have been other animals there ... or none at all.

5 Yes
It was the only safe place to lay the baby. All his life, Jesus was content to live with few belongings. He was brought up in a humble family and he always paid a lot of attention to the poor. (Luke 2, v 7)

6 Yes
When the angels gave them the news, the shepherds from the Bethlehem area made their way to the stable. The first people who came to see Jesus were poor. (Luke 2, v 8 – 16)

7 Yes
The shepherds were spending the night in the fields guarding their flocks. (Luke 2, v 8)

20

No

They were probably wise men who studied the stars, like astronomers.

No

The Bible does not mention how many of them there were, nor their names, where they came from, or their colour.

0 No

We celebrate the Epiphany at this time of year, but the Bible does not say when the wise men came.

1 Romans

The whole of Palestine was under the control of the Romans for about sixty years.

2 Yes

Gold, frankincense and myrrh are royal gifts.

3 Yes

Matthew 2, v 16 –18

you have scored:

0 – 13 points: Well done! You can't be caught out on the story of esus' birth. Next time you see a crib, you can tell other people verything you know!

– 9 points: You certainly know some of the Christmas story. For the est of the questions, you had a one in two chance of getting the right nswer. Try to remember the answers and do the quiz again. You are ound to do better!

points or less: No, Jesus is not the son of Father Christmas and he vas not born in Brighton. Read the Bible story again; you will be urprised!

ANSWERS

| Page 1: | 1 FATHER; 2 ANGELS; 3 ISAIAH; 4 SHEPHERDS; 5 DAVID; 6 MARY; 7 BETHLEHEM; 8 MICAH; 9 STAR; 10 PROPHETS; 11 SON; 12 CHRISTMAS |

Page 1:   1 FATHER; 2 ANGELS; 3 ISAIAH; 4 SHEPHERDS;
          5 DAVID; 6 MARY; 7 BETHLEHEM; 8 MICAH;
          9 STAR; 10 PROPHETS; 11 SON; 12 CHRISTMAS

Page 3:   C.

Page 4:   A4 – B5 – C1 – D2 – E3

Page 5:   15 men. 2 women, 2 children, 19 animals
          (including 1 bird)

Page 8:   23 sheep

Page 9:   D

Page 10: Lord, you have kept your promise... With my
          own eyes I have seen your salvation. (Luke 2,
          v29-30)

Page 15: between 90 and 100 km

Page 18: A - Joseph, B - Simon, C - Jude, D - James

22

A BOY GROWING UP

During his childhood and teenage years, Jesus lives with his parents. He learns how to be a carpenter from his father. It's hard work. To learn properly, Jesus copies his father's actions carefully.

See how carefully you can copy this drawing on the squares below.

23

© 2001 Scripture Union, 207-209 Queensway, Bletchley, Milton Keynes, Buckinghamshire MK2 2EB, England

First published 2001
Reprinted 2001, 2003

Designed and retold by Ginobi, illustrated by J. Maré. Originally published by Husky Productions, in French as *Sur les traces de Noel*, Copyright 1999 Husky Productions F-26120 Peyrus.
All rights reserved.

Translated and adapted from the French by Rosemary North.

ISBN 1 85999 518 7

All Bible quotations are taken from the CEV (Contemporary English Version) published by Bible Society and used with permission.

Scripture Union is an international Christian charity working with churches in more than 150 countries, providing resources to bring the good news about Jesus Christ to children, young people and families and to encourage them to develop spirituality through the Bible and prayer.

As well as our network of volunteers, staff and associates who run holidays, church based events and school Christian groups, we produce a wide range of publications and support those who use our resources through training programmes.